G000090972

My

Original

Sin

Marie-Victoire
Rouillier

My

Original

Sin

Translated by Alan José

BLACK SPRING PRESS

First English-Language Edition
Black Spring Press, 1994

ISBN 0 948238 17 8

© Marie-Victoire Rouillier 1988
Translation © Alan José, 1994

Black Spring Press Ltd, 63 Harlescott Road, London
SE15 3DA

First published in France by Editions Alinea, 1988

Jacket designed by Pete Rozycki
Typeset in Great Britain by Hewer Text, Edinburgh
Printed in Great Britain by Antony Rowe Ltd

To Marie-Andrée, for whom these letters were not intended, but without whom they could not have been written.

Everything blurs, and nothing comes near to you,
Not my heart, nor my hands, nor the words
  that I say.
Untouched you just go on your own quiet way,
And what I have said has never been clear to
  you

L. Aragon

You start the forty days of Lent, in your ice-cold convent, receiving neither visitors nor letters, and whilst you settle into the comfortable intimacy of a God made to your own measure, I stay in the wilderness. And there I can hear only your silence, exactly as it has been for forty years. A silence consisting of conventional words, of decorous affection, without flesh and without warmth. You have given yourself body and soul to a 'higher cause': whilst I still stand at the edge of the abyss, between your God of love and my own demons of hatred and fear.

I idealised you for years; then I waited for a gesture, which never came. Finally I decided to look at you squarely, just as you are. But you seem to exist only by virtue of the images in which I myself attempted to hold you. I see nothing other than myself, weighed down painfully by my protective shells, by all my despair. Will I never be able to hate you without injuring myself? Like Emmanuelle, I wanted to escape from your love but, like her, all I can do is scream.

When I learned that she had attacked you I was pleased; but today she is in an institution, and so her struggle has been of no avail, not even to make you dislike her; for you continue to love her, I am sure, just as you love me and the rest of mankind.

But why must your love be always so all-embracing? What am I to do with those thousands of lost souls, whom I drag along protectively with my own body, right into your heart? What am I to do with your goodness when I need to be wanted? What does your wisdom matter to me when I am sinking into madness? In spite of your efforts, you have never known how to love me, so could you not today make an effort to rejoin me in new ways, ways that are not so impenetrable as those of Our Lord?

If I have never been able to tear you away

from your prayers, will I be able, one day,
to make you dislike me so that finally I am
alone in your hatred?

Thursday 21 February

Thirty-nine days yet, before the holy rule of your convent authorises you to come back into communication with the rest of the world; thirty-nine days in which I can write to you without your being able to read what I have written; thirty-nine days of impunity, in which I can finally shout out my hatred to you without your forgiving me, in which I can demand everything of you and be sure that I will get nothing: no more waiting, exhausted, to receive at the end of my dark night tokens of love which leave me with my hunger. I will no longer have to make up excuses for your affectionate lack of warmth, for your way of looking at me without seeing me.

So, for forty days, you have absolutely no control over the distance which separates us: you are protected by an anachronistic rule which is as absurd as my own uncontrollable impulses. You withdraw into the wilderness, like Christ, ready to confront the demons of your temptations . . . Mine are not hunger or thirst, but a never-ending childhood, with death all around me, even in your very look.

I resisted as best I could, not knowing that the struggles of the soul are intended to be lost. Then I sought refuge in faith: a faith which attached me to you, as a hanged man is held by his tree. You carried me in your branches without understanding that you were turning me into a skeleton. But I stayed alive, perhaps simply because I adored you.

Will you ever know how much I wanted you? This desire is the better part of me, but for such a long time now it has frightened me, so that I still dare not look at it.

How can you choose to fall back into silence whilst I am waiting for you to talk to me? How can you be filled with your God, when without you I am empty? How can you transcend in love for mankind the hatred which I have for you?

Happily, you cannot reply to me; you would be quite capable of talking to me of God, where all I can see is an enormous delusion. And do not tell me that you love me: each time I believed you I fell sick. At present I no longer have need of you to be that. Unable to accustom myself to your presence, as you were never there, my body became used to sickness. Since then, I have learned to imitate you, and I keep up appearances.

You could never stifle me with your kisses, even from a distance, but you knew how to keep me a prisoner in the iron grip of your good education. So then I hid my unhappiness, my crises of faith, my crises of tears, and although totally lacking in charm and allurement, I learned how to search around me for genuine sympathy, so that I might forget that I was crazed with love for you. I created for myself the semblance of ordinary happiness, of real dynamism, which you welcomed with satisfaction, never guessing just how far I was deceiving myself. You sometimes even pressed me to your heart, as if with pride, and all I could feel were the five layers of coarse cloth which separated me from your flesh. As for the tender words with which you wanted to lull me, they seemed always to be formal prayers addressed to God, rather than to myself.

Today I leave you to the mortification of your prayers and your total devotion to your good intentions, so that I may better explore my hatred, this crowning emotion which still binds me to you.

I have just returned from the psychiatric hospital, where I went to visit Emmanuelle; I found her diminished, dulled, she who used to be so alive. Previously, by the way, she used to impress me by her abrupt way of resisting your affection. I, by contrast, was reduced to helplessness.

When we had to visit you, all my attention was concentrated on the moment when you would appear and when you would open your arms to me. The rest of my life was merely a parenthesis hung around this image, the reality of which became painful by being distorted. For next to you, in your arms which enfolded me so badly, I felt like a corpse. My skin, which was never joined with yours, was stretched over a heart as disembodied as those flaccid and bleeding organs which are displayed in the windows of butchers' shops. It seemed to me that this meat belonged to my own flesh; because the food which I thought I would never finish chewing, so as to grow big and strong, returned whence it came, each time I swallowed, into the inner recesses of my entrails, precisely there where the secret of death must be concealed, along with everything else which absorbed me.

With your gentle voice and your persuasive look, you said to me one day: 'God is within you.' At first I was afraid, as you had adopted the tone of voice people use when they are about to announce a catastrophe, but afterwards I imagined your God as a soft and flabby lump of meat, which I must perforce chew over for hours on end.

On the other hand, I marvelled at the hosts at Mass: white, like you, almost transparent, they melted softly on the tongue and disappeared in the kisses of my saliva. I felt that I was in communion with you, and at night, in my bed, I imagined a thousand heroic deaths near to you, so that I might finally have the right to disappear in the arms of your embrace. I kept alive these nightly perils with all my childish strength, because by dying in this way I could at one and the same time both flee from

you and find you again, be filled with your
presence and continue to want you.

I do not know what Emmanuelle's dreams
were at this time; one thing that I am certain
of is that she was stronger than I was. She
did not spend hours getting herself ready, as
if for a ball, before going to visit you, and
she did not tremble with impatience. One
night, after we had spent several hours with
you, and I was crying, alone in my bed, she
came to me and held me close to her, saying:
'You must not expect so much from her; she
cannot give you any more; we shall never be
for her anything other than an intention in her
prayers.'

She was older than I, and was often right,
but I was incapable of resigning myself to
expecting nothing further from you. For
her, on the other hand, it seemed as though
you did not matter, and I thought she was
invulnerable.

And then, when she flung herself at you,
I understood my mistake. You destroyed her
also by degrees, with the violence of your
good feelings in which you took refuge in
order not to hear the appeal which we, she

and I, dared not put into words. You thought you loved us, but you struck us violently with your holiness, just like a blow, driving Emmanuelle to madness and me to despair.

You paralyse even my memories. There is nothing left of my childhood, other than your interminable absences. I remember a card you sent to me for my first Communion; it was a lovely picture, a vast empty landscape with a large sun shining: everything that I loathe today, and which makes me seek refuge in darkened cinemas, where the film distils a world suited to my own limitations. It was there that I learned to love intangible figures which, like you, disappeared at the end of an hour or two.

But with this card, for once, you over-whelmed me in a few lines. At the bottom you sent me kisses, from a distance, without taking any risks, as always. And I also imitated you; for years I sent kisses in my letters to friends to whom I did not dare open my arms, for I imagined that it was not possible to hug a woman one loved without dying.

Just above your signature, you had added 'Soon!' This was more than I needed to plunge me into feverish anticipation, because I regarded everything you said as the gospel truth, and abided by it body and soul. 'Soon' meant that after I had been to bed two or three times, or at the latest after next Sunday's Mass, I would find you again, would be able to be seen by you, and perhaps, for a burning instant, feel your lips on the corner of my eyes, for that was where you used to kiss me. But more than a hundred sermons passed before I saw you again.

At the beginning, I went to church fervently. As you lived in a convent, I understood that God had a privileged relationship with you, and my prayers to him were in fact declarations of love which I destined secretly for you. It was a passionate language, which I could never have invented myself, and which was a thousand times more beautiful than poetry at school. These prayers, using phrases of infinity, as deep as breath, were all the more dazzling as I did not understand them too well. I have to admit that I was barely ten years old, but this did

not prevent me from repeating fervently
each night:

> *May He curb our tongue*
> *to save us from the horror of discord;*
> *may He cover our eyes with a veil*
> *to keep us from worldly vanities;*
> *may He keep our hearts pure,*
> *protect us from the seductions*
> *of the world; and may the pride*
> *of our flesh be overcome*
> *by abstinence and by sobriety.*

The general sense escaped me, but the words
'horror', 'discord', 'seduction' and 'pride' suggested a means of containing my emotions.
Nothing was too strong to pull me towards
you. If the fear of loving you stiffened all my
limbs, it nevertheless inflamed my imagination and my speech. I was like a tree, blown
by the wind, always held down by its roots,
but full of sap, of the sky, and of sound.

Three years later, when I saw you, I was
beaten, dry. My appeals to you had been so
long unanswered that I felt finally abandoned

by God and by women. The enthusiastic faith of my childhood, that faith which made me believe in you, was replaced by a hankering for emptiness, and the uneasy fear of sin. I no longer sought you in my prayers, I wanted only to prove that I could do without you. I went to Mass, even on weekdays, because it was a mysterious celebration, completely foreign to my daily life. As children do today by watching television, as adults do at work, I sought in the church a refuge against myself.

In this warm and dark cavern, where I retreated, on my knees, lulled by the muffled sounds of the faithful, I chanted the strange phrases without thinking of anything. I did not want to see you again, I had no desire to weep, I felt nothing, I was barely alive, and it was good that it was so. I armed myself therefore as best I could, against you, against myself, so as to curtail my suffering, but gradually this empty fortress was occupied, as if by a guard dog, by the feeling of my guilt. The desire which had borne me towards you without finding an outlet now yielded to shame. I thought myself cowardly for wanting you still, for imagining myself next to you with this body which was still not fully grown, and which never again could be coiled in your arms.

My original sin was to need you who could live without me, was to talk to you at night without hearing you, was to feel your gaze which had never been able to see me, was to touch your hand which you kept beneath your rough serge, and to place my lips on it, feeling a wild palpitation in the pit of my stomach. But the more I dreamed of you, the more I was alone, and the more sterile my prayers became. I believed I had been walking towards God and, like Achilles, I was 'stationary with great strides.'

Today, when I had hoped to rid myself of those old demons at the stroke of a pen, by telling you how much I love you and how much I hate you, I discover that the traces of these forty letters of Lent are already half obliterated. I have to relive it all, to untie my past to the point of agony, before I can be reborn in myself, far away from you, well beyond my dreams and my remorse.

I imagine that you are comfortable in the cold, in your icy convent where you mortify your flesh and your senses. Does the world which weighs on you become more bearable during your hibernation? You shiver in peace, whilst I burn in anguish and in hatred. I cannot bear your serenity; I cannot bear that you should embody a happiness which eludes me.

Have you ever thought that to be a model for others is to be an object of hatred? If I had not known you, I should no doubt never have wished to be like you; it would have been enough to cultivate compliance and cowardice, and perhaps I should have suffered less. But I did want to be like you, to become what you were, so as to be two people at once, and to be self-sufficient, since I despaired of drawing you to me. I succeeded only in creating for myself an inaccessible ideal, like you, of which I am now unable to rid myself. As soon as anger fades from my heart, I believe once again in goodwill, in humour, in lucidity; and yet I was born to be an alcoholic, or a torturer, or to die. But you planted a fuse in the very depths of my being, and now, because I cannot be as perfect as you are, I want to go mad, like Emmanuelle. Alas, I never cease to cry out between your two silences, without ever finding my way.

Whilst I struggle, so as not to be able to see anything further, you listen to the world from the depths of your prayer. Is it a world like that of the down and outs whom I pass each day, and on whom the certainties with which I have fed my hatred for ten years collapse? I espoused all the angry causes, everything to make me vomit up our society, and then I finally discovered that it was not the hunger of the poor which disturbed my digestion. I thought I was weeping for others, but it was myself that I was taking pity on. Could you not have done it for me? Could you not have loved me so that I might cease to hate?

'When Christ arrives at your door, He is always dirty and down at heel', the parish priest of my childhood used to say, sharing

his roof with the vagrants who passed by.
With you He became seductive, and that is
much worse, especially as He is faithful to
his motto: always present, but never there!
First you invaded my desires, and now you
pursue me even in my renunciations. I wanted
to settle the account of my rancour, to send
you not letters but bills to be paid with your
blood. All of the spites aroused within me
were to conclude with the same phrase: 'I
shall never forgive you!' This violence, which
throws me to the floor, forces me nevertheless
back to you in a slow sequence of prostration:
struck down as I am by the premonition that,
one day or another day, your goodness will
overcome my hatred.

Sixth letter; on the sixth day, God created
man and woman to reign over the earth and
the animals. Will I, one day, be able to reign
over myself? Will I be able, like the earth, to
emerge from the sea, and to separate myself
from you? I try to consolidate my inner core,
but with each new page the mud carries it
away. My letters are a flow of lava, a huge
load of soft clay, bringing right to you the fire
which consumes me. But when I have reached
you, when I have come down to the bottom
of my slope, in forty days, will you be able to
recognise behind these petrified lines the desire
which bends me towards you? Will I be able to
reach you anyway, deep within your desert,
when I set off thirty years too late?

You fast before going to Communion, and I
never cease to vomit up a past which imprisons
me. I am like a funambulist on the torn thread
of my childhood. Let me melt into you, be

buried deep within your bosom, build for myself a refuge in your arms; let me find my breath in your breath, and create for myself a language in the words of love which you have never said; let my eyelids be sewn beneath your kisses, so that finally I can see myself in your eyes.

I ought to have said this to you more than thirty years ago, but I had to wait until it was too late before daring to open my mouth. Too late, yes . . . I am no longer even capable of imagining myself in your arms: the harshness of your habit and the rigidity of my fears would give our embraces a derisory austerity; our outpourings would be nothing but a liturgy without music.

And then I want to fly with my own wings, those wings which you have clipped with the parsimony of your love.

I have been back to see Emmanuelle. She has come out of her mutism. We talked, we even cried together, as if to recapture that lost time, the time when we were condemned to be happy in order to please you. This was your way of making us pay for your love. You never wept, and we had to hold back our tears, whilst with you everything smelt of death, even your kisses. And with them you tried to instil in us the image of an ideal mother, that of your twin sister who died at my birth.

No one was to blame for her disappearance, but in order to escape from despair you determined to give a meaning to this absence: we were obliged, throughout our childhood, to show ourselves worthy of the love of a mother who was never there, and whom you never wished to replace.

My father loved you, and you knew it; but

you entered the convent, and he married your sister. When she died, you undoubtedly wept a great deal, and prayed a great deal, but you abandoned us. You had not taken your final vows; you were bound by no oath; but you had no doubts about your vocation. Being ready to listen to God, who loved you but did not need you, was less disturbing than listening to a man's desire, a man to whom you were certainly not indifferent.

You were already cultivating that benevolent serenity which fascinates me and which I also curse, since because of it you entrusted me to the goodness of a God for whom I had no use, instead of taking me in your arms and watching over me. You played the heroine instead of coming down from your pedestal, and rolling up your sleeves. You misjudged the world and morality. That shining saintliness, which you constructed stone by stone, is based on two ruined lives for which you were not even responsible: Emmanuelle is in a mental hospital and, as for myself, I cannot be reborn. Emmanuelle's tears yesterday brought to mind other tears, long ago. I have retained a vivid picture of them, to which I thought I had become hardened: the image of my father sobbing over his desk, behind the half-open door. I had never seen him cry, any more than I had ever heard him raise his voice or swear. He was a rock of impenetrable granite who, although unable to envelop us in his feelings, at least gave us the impression of an indestructible presence.

This grief did more than simply shock and distress me: it released within me a horrible reflex for survival. I thought I would protect myself by concealing my emotions, and so I hid inside myself, within this sinister prison from which I can now no longer escape. This instinct for survival is without doubt the worst of instincts: it transforms us into the living dead, it instils in us the fear that we can no longer face the external world. And against this slow process of fossilization we have no recourse other than our poor intelligence, this spider's web fastened to our fears. I tried as others have done to immerse myself in study, but I find myself this evening just as lost as I was thirty years ago when I saw you leaving my father's study.

I do not know why he broke down, but I

do remember that you were there, that you had spent the afternoon with us, and that once again you abandoned us. Basically I understand that you needed to choose the religious life; you are certainly in God's camp. You reveal yourself long enough to awaken in us a call to love, to a deeper life, and then you disappear; and where all we had to do was to distil the mediocrity of the daily round, you replaced that with chaos and desire.

Will I be able one day to see it all clearly? Will I be able to understand why you are the only one who symbolises everything I detest and everything I love?

I should like to go down into my own being, moving at the same time far away from you; but I do not know what detour to take. And then before entering deep into that mire which you have left within me, I should not be sorry, in spite of its being years too late, to bring to your eyes the tears which have stuck in my throat: it would be your turn to have your sight clouded, after having left me voiceless.

Did you cry? I am drying up. I feel in general
a sense of satisfaction when I have been able
to deluge you with my reproaches, but it
does not last. I should like to believe that
I have no gift for hatred, and that in the
end your love will carry me beyond myself,
beyond this life, my loathing for which is
so intensely reciprocated. Yet I never cease
to demand a reckoning from you. Having
been unable to live by your love, I want at
least to have you share my troubles. How
long must I pay in vomiting for the tears
which I have held back because of you?
How many migraines will crush my skull
and wipe away from my forehead the trace
of your kisses, devoid of desire and lifeless?
For how long must I imagine my fingernails
being wrenched out because I never dared
to feel the touch of your skin beneath my
hand? And what must I do with this body

of mine which you have never held tight in your arms?

It is not a religion that you have chosen, it is a perpetual renunciation, and you never thought that someone would have to pay for it . . . I would rather it had been you.

You never understood anything, dazzled as you were by your God, the only good that you wanted to share with me. And I too, in my fervour, saw only fire there. After the family prayers I wanted to learn my missal by heart, to swallow it down. I started with the last of the gospels, St John:

> In the beginning was the Word:
> the Word was with God
> and the Word was God.

It was a promising start, a total fusion beyond words; as it continued it obviously became spoiled, but I was unable to imagine that it could be otherwise. With you everything brought me back to despair, and I relapsed into your love as if into a sickness.

I was growing up, however, and I was learning to hold myself stiff and straight, but I could neither see nor hear: my eyes sought only the eyes of others, and my ears heard only those things which brought back my mother's voice. I was missing her, whilst you, you were turned towards God. For years I continued the pretence of living; everywhere I felt ill at ease, I watched carefully what I said and did, but people thought I was well brought up. In the main I was merely the product of your absence, and my faults were held down by an iron band of principles.

Emmanuelle, by comparison, appeared more serene. She dazzled me when she adopted such a detached air. One day when I was talking warmly about you, she gave me a withering smile:

'And are you wanting to become a saint as well?'

Then, so as not to be embarrassed by her bantering, I decided suddenly that would be my vocation.

I did not know what sanctity consisted of, but it appeared to derive from an impossible, inadmissible love, like that which nailed me firmly to you. But over and above that agony, it seemed right to imagine some vague form of resurrection, and this I rejected at all costs. It might be acceptable for you to imagine an after-life as an extension of an existence which you love so much, but in my case my only desire is to hate you until it destroys me. Another life would run the risk of crushing my resistance, and I should end by forgiving you, perhaps even by recognising that it was you who were right. Once again you would triumph: but after having been your victim, I have no wish to become your ally.

You always treated me like an adult. You were very proud of this, I imagine, as are all those who abide by principles. In any case, even had you treated me otherwise, I would surely have found good reason for reproaching you with it.

And yet this was a sinister present to give me. You claimed to respect me, but you obliged me to say what it pleased you to hear. You see me as courageous when I am merely a larva, as generous when I loathe you, as intelligent when I have not even learned to support myself.

You forced me to swallow my lies, making me believe that they were fine, for you were incapable of accepting me with my terrors, with my desires. All your psychological theories only serve to produce generations of unhappy cretins like me. So stop treating me as an adult, if you claim to love me, do not imprison me in so derisory a part.

I have no strength left, and when I think of you, I feel myself regenerated, only to sink back once again. I no longer want to dazzle you with the gloss of my knowledge, to comfort you with my intellectual enthusiasms, to beguile you with my apparent steadfastness. Just let me finally be a child, near to you; let me stay silent to the point of anguish, and weep into oblivion. Love me with your eyes, with your lips, with your skin, and do not put up between us another barricade of vain words.

Yet once you spoke the truth to me; once only. In a chilly half-light, you dared to leave the comfortable path of your anecdotes, and reveal yourself with your doubts. You said:

'Loving Christ is also a way for me to escape from the memory of death.'

And hearing you say this, I felt myself alive with a great internal fire which burned my ears and brought me to the verge of rapture. I was no longer rigid with cold, but like a swimmer resting, floating gently, bound to your voice by every pore in my skin. Never before had I felt, as I did on this occasion, the life of someone else flowing into mine, saturating my heart and my veins, and ridding me of all my fears.

Since then I have known other intimacies, more amorous and more carnal, but it is nevertheless this exchange of words which I strive day after day to re-create. Other moments of mutual fusion have been granted to me, faithfully, like a pledge of happiness; I have no need to exhaust myself desiring them in order to escape from myself; but these words, scarcely formed between us, transported me to a world so full of promise that I seek to renew them at every opportunity. This vampire-like appetite has driven away many friends, reluctant to give me their words to feed on. Others, however, consent to talk to me, to give me a little of their life, so that I can be avenged for all the absences to which you subjected me through the words you blotted out and the emotions you buried. They have enabled me to rediscover my own emotions, and more than that: without knowing it, they help to kill this image of you which I carry inside myself like a cancer.

Saturday 2 March

Will I ever recover from your absences, from your rejections? You rarely talked to me; often you made me keep silent, not by interrupting me, of course, but by making me conceal what I expected of you.

One day – I must have been about fifteen, as it was shortly before we left for Spain – I stared at you intently, without answering your questions, imitating perhaps some banal cinema seducer, and you said to me: 'Don't look at me like that, stop day-dreaming, answer me.'

I lowered my eyes, and like a sleepwalker entered into your insipid and decorous world. I understood then that everything which I had felt so far was as nothing compared to what I was suddenly experiencing: a vertiginous longing to die.

Some years later, after we had returned to France, scarcely a night passed when the idea of death did not awake in me like a battering-ram. Because at that time I did not dare to detest you, to spit in your face, to claw it as Emmanuelle did recently; I despise myself every day for being unable to commit suicide. And my body persists in compensating for this cowardice by suffering.

Each time I lift up my eyes to an imaginary mother I can talk fluently, even brilliantly, but in the loneliness of my room, every one of my words weighs like a regret. I resent being unable to sink into silence, and like Penelope I spend my nights unpicking methodically, thread by thread, the fabric of the day which forces me to live.

When you reply to me, if you ever do, will you serve up to me a pretty couplet on the value of life? That is normally the last refuge of well-meaning folk with a broken spirit, when they no longer dare strike their concrete God. That type of humanism is beatitude without grace, it is Saint-Exupéry versus Racine.

'Loving is not looking at one another, it is looking together in the same direction.' That was what you used to say to me, speaking of things you do not understand,

but I prefer the farewells of Antiochus to
Berenice:

> *Farewell, then, what should I say to you?*
> *From heedless looks I flee*
> *Which, seeing me always, never did see me.*
> *Farewell. I go, your image o'erflows my*
> *   heart:*
> *So I shall wait, still loving you, that death*
> *   which is my part.*

From two centuries away, Racine speaks
to me as if he had understood in advance
everything I was going to feel. His verses
enchant me like music and move me like
a whispered secret; but you who claim to
love me, you look at me as you would a
dead person, and you encumber my heart
with your virtuous comfort.

Emmanuelle has talked to me again. We spent a long time together. She is going to leave the hospital. She told me about the last time father visited her.

A few days before she came to stay and recuperate near to you, he came to see her. In the evening she drove him home in the car, listening to James Bowman singing *Orlando Furioso* by Vivaldi. The voice of this counter-tenor, full of an equivocal sensuality, but with such a pure and clear tone, moved her very deeply.

Suddenly my father turned off the music with an irritable gesture. Emmanuelle had difficulty in containing herself. She felt like making him get out, and leaving him on the empty road to find his own way home. She could not bear it that this man was still asserting his right to dominate her life even in her own car. With rage in her heart, she leaned forward to the tape in order to turn it on again. It was at that moment that the accident happened.

You know the rest: father's death, Emmanuelle's depression, and your offer to provide her for a short time with a comfortable haven. What you do not know is what was tormenting her and preventing her from speaking. And the more you were ready to listen to her, the more deeply she plunged into her silence. One morning, however, she did try to explain: 'I have killed my father,' she said, before falling back into mutism.

Had she been able to continue, she would have explained that, without even admitting it to herself, she had wished him dead. But your goodness blinded you once more, and you wanted to reassure her. So whilst you were proving to her that she had nothing to reproach herself with, you were preventing her from saying what she reproached father with. This accident revealed her true feelings to herself, and you, you distorted them by wanting to embellish them. It was at that moment that she suddenly howled and jumped at your throat, lacerating you with her nails.

These scars that you bear are not the stigmata of your goodness, but the marks of a hatred which you have never dared to face. There is no doubt that both she and I have a lot of misunderstandings to unravel with you, unless it is too late and you cannot bear to hear anything further about them.

But this evening I shall not take up her anger again and add it to my own. In any event, as soon as Emmanuelle demonstrates the least aggression towards you, I feel my tenderness for you being reborn. And if my love cannot reach you, I should like to have at least the privilege of hatred. I should like to wipe away, with my fingers and with my lips, those puffy scars on your face, because they are not mine.

What marks can I gouge out deep within you, I who know only how to lacerate myself? Do not leave me alone. I need you; I need you to clasp me in your arms at least once, and to tell me that you love me. I no longer want to have to guess at it; I no longer want my awakened senses exhausted by trying to insinuate my way into your affection. I want the proof and the delirium, I want to be destroyed by the deluge of your love and not by your wisdom. Stop being the sole incarnation of all divine love, stop coming to me as if you were the guardian of the world's goodness, stop wanting my well-being. I don't give a damn for your God who always comes between us. And if you absolutely must want him to save us, then at least please want first to lose yourself with me.

Quousque tandem abutere, Catilina, patienta nostra?
For how long, Catilina, will you abuse our
patience? I have never understood any Latin,
and particularly the orations of Cicero. By
and large his thinking goes beyond my own
intellectual ability. He talks neither of love
nor of death nor of desire; so I could never
see where it was all leading. I even believed
in all sincerity that he wrote only with the
intention of being a nuisance to generations of
schoolchildren. Yet this famous tag stayed in
my mind, because I used to repeat it out loud in
my room, like a challenge, without suspecting
that it was you I was addressing it to.

Besides, did I ever succeed in learning
anything at school which was not intended
to bring me closer to you or to take me
further away from you? So Latin could never
be anything other than a lost cause for me,
since it was the language of your divine office,

the language which put you in direct communication with God, and placed you far away
from me in an incomprehensible world.

You did not only prey upon my mind;
my feelings also developed in your wake
and bound me to you. This morning, in
the smell of a clean, damp sheet, I got
a sudden whiff of my childhood: that of
foreign nannies who carried me in their
arms, in their cotton garments. When they
returned to their own country, their odour
was mingled with yours, with that of your
habit, which gave off a combination of incense
and floor-polish. Sometimes I would close my
eyes to rediscover the contact of their breasts,
of their arms which cradled me, but when I
re-opened them I found nothing there; and
when, by chance, you were close to me, your
body remained stiff and distant.

This was before you left me for three whole
years, and when you did leave, all I could do
was cry. Later I began to detest you, when I
came to understand that your love consisted
of empty words, and that you were saving
yourself for God and your convent. Had I been
able to make my hatred fall upon you, I should

have saved myself years of unhappiness and these forty litanies which I am writing much too late.

But how could I detest you when you did everything to captivate me? If only you had been acting on your own behalf, from pure selfishness, we might have understood each other. I also would have had the occasion to fascinate you, but your voice and your smile had only one purpose, which was to lead me to God, and so inevitably the charm that I tried to put on for you never achieved its goal.

You betrayed my confidence, you perverted my love, and you sold me to God, body and soul, as a pimp would have done.

Wednesday 6 March

Your odour follows me even in my anger. I thought that by detesting you I would rid myself of you, but it is you who are going to succeed with me: I shall die or go mad. I can of course control myself, I even manage to do some work, but this irreparable split between the life I lead and the obsessions which assail me seems to grow wider each day. I look emptiness in the face, and you bravely keep your eyes closed on your prayers.

If, like you, I could allow myself to be absorbed by an imaginary love, I could perhaps forget everything, but I am no longer capable, alas, of living beyond my obsessions, as others live beyond their means.

This cotton sheet, which has been hanging at my window for the last two days, dampened by the showers, takes me straight back to my childhood, to that time when I had no horizons other than you. I wonder sometimes if I was not actually seeking in you a particular odour, that of my mother, your twin sister. In any event you took her place a little too late: you snatched me from death by taking me in your arms, when for days I had refused all nourishment. You gave me back my sense of smell and of touch, but scarcely had I started to eat again than you disappeared. And so, cast back upon the shores of existence, I yearn just as much for the waters of death as for the breath of life.

Would I have pursued you with my hatred and my attentions if you had become a solid mother of a family like all the rest? I do not know, but I think I should have felt less abandoned, as I cannot help thinking that you chose God instead of me, instead of Emmanuelle, instead of my father, just to invent for yourself a love which suited you, and in which we scarcely figured.

When I was a child I decked you out in all the virtues; when I looked at you, I put an imaginary halo over your head, like those statues of the Madonna with a slightly sad look, their eyes gazing down on us. I had no doubt that your vocation was the result of a

divine call, like the voices of Joan of Arc: if
you had entered the convent it was to fulfil
a great destiny. Now I doubt it, I wonder if
you did not choose God as I chose you, on
the basis of a guess, as a child might. I only
know that I shall never become an adult until
I learn to detach myself from you.

Why did you withdraw to a place where
there was no room for me? Why did you hand
on to me an ideal when I needed your caresses?
Thanks to your prayers, I have become a sick
head on a body filled with pain. I would rather
not have known you than have idealised you
behind the grilles of a convent parlour. Your
religion has done me more harm than the
disappearance of my mother: at least with
her I know that this part of myself has died;
with you, I never cease being crucified in the
hope of an improbable resurrection.

Will you speak to me again, as you spoke to me on that previous occasion? If there is one request behind all these letters of rejection, it can only be this: speak to me, from the depths of yourself, with your doubts and your weaknesses. I do not ask you to be interested in me, but to need me. Do not seek to weigh me down with your acts of kindness: today your strength and your charity make me sick, and will never be able to replace the breast and the milk that you could not give me in the past.

Keep your well-meaning words for the other sisters – they do not expect any comfort. But I have not reached that point yet. Do not push me towards an uncertain future whilst I am still struggling with my birth. Death is very near: I long to plunge into it, and not towards the life which you hold out to me.

Why are your words, your confidences,

so necessary to me? I have no vocation as a confessor, and it is certainly not my intention to give you absolution. It is not only the intensity of these moments which makes them so indispensable to me; it is no longer even a question of pleasure, but of survival: it is as if I were kneaded into these words which give me shape and stability. But whilst I wait in vain for these exchanges, I collapse like a sack of grain which has been gnawed away by a horde of rats.

Yet what common link is there in the tortured confessions of all the women who have talked to me?

The voice, perhaps: the inimitable sound of a word hanging in suspense which has nothing to contribute other than a need for silence. When these voices reach me they are all suppressed, like the voice of my mother which echoed within her swollen belly, or the voice of her death rattle on the hospital bed where I had been put down near to her.

It is therefore to this border area between life and death that I am led by the murmured confessions of friends who surrender for a moment to become just the shadow of themselves. It is in these darkened regions that I must find my own feet and gather up my strength. But you, all you can think of is dragging me into the light and there blinding me with your certainties.

There was almost a sequel to our first exchange, during which you really talked to me. I had waited a month, right up to the very limit of my endurance, before coming back to you, as you had suggested.

We were chatting in stifled words, sitting in a corner of that large room full of gleaming woodwork, where you received your visitors. I tried to let myself be carried along by the flow of our sentences, so as to avoid precipitating anything, not asking questions which might have led you to seek refuge behind your habitual way of speaking. Gradually your voice became more serious, your words more hesitant; we were slowly getting near to the sort of confidences where you would appear disarmed, vulnerable, and suffering from an unbearable absence which had deprived you, like me, of part of yourself.

But a sister came in, busying herself near to

us with her imaginary activities and crowd-
ing us with her useless smiles. Your voice
regained its tone of assurance, as if relieved
by this importunate presence. We exchanged
a few polite banalities, whilst a fit of nervous
trembling made me want to cry. My anger
helped me not to give way to it. I would
willingly have killed this church rat on the
spot, living off the warmth of others. She
saw me turn pale; and in her haste to offer
me her help, she broke a vase, which created
a diversion, and saved me from her unbearable
solicitude. And whilst she busied herself with
your help, I was terrified by the ravages of my
emotion, and in despair when I saw that you
were not even troubled by it.

Your determination not to understand anything was so great that I could have died beside
you without your being able to help me. How
could you live after having destroyed me so
utterly? How could you get back to the river
bank so easily, whilst I was being swept away
by the current? Once again I had narrowly
escaped death in your presence, and because
this descent under your protection had miscar-
ried, I could never again be truly reborn . . .

How many times since then have I tried,
with other people, to allow myself to be pulled
towards this fracture which gapes within me?
Occasionally it has happened, but the only
thing I can really recall is the expectation
which has followed those rare moments when
I have been filled to overflowing. When new
dialogues I hoped for did not come about, I
then sensed even more strongly the quivering
rebirth of my interior demons, and the fear
of awakening them made me feel so bad that
I forced myself to turn my back on such
moments. When I contribute to my own
unhappiness, the pain is at least known to
me; and if I am waiting to die, I do not feel a
stranger in a strange land. But if it is someone
else who avoids my desires, where might
my anger cease? Will I not want to kill
her in my madness? Did I not want to kill my
mother, who never responded to my cries?
And how is it possible to want to kill a dead
person?

Unquestionably I prefer to hate myself
rather than continue to explore my hatred
of you, because you risk disturbing the
last bastion of my dreams: the obsessive

and unchanging image of a perfect mother who existed only in the projection of my desires.

Emmanuelle has committed suicide. As might be expected, she made a thorough job of it: some sleeping pills plus a bullet, to ensure that she did not fail in her final enterprise. No question for her of calling for help by leaving herself a possible way out. Neither you nor I can do anything more for her.

Yet another of my supports collapses with her. Her depression had already unsettled some of the stable images of my childhood, but I thought that I could rediscover her, start again with her. As the difference in our ages no longer mattered, I might have been able to take up a place at her side as a real adult. She was my only ally against you, the one who could understand and share my feelings about you without any need for explanation.

So I am your only family, and now nothing protects me from your devastating love, there are no more ramparts, no more refuges. I

do not really want even to face it: I only
regret that I did not have the courage to do
what Emmanuelle has done. I am torn by
envy as well as by pain; once again I feel
cowardly and weak by comparison with her,
who stated in advance a definitive, dazzling
'no' to everything which you still might have
wished for her.

Her implacable silence seems to me louder
than all my cries, and she will no longer be
trying, as I do, to interpret the signs which
you would certainly have given her. She has
chosen the better part, and I am ashamed to
have allowed her, once again, to precede me.
Because for me it is now very late: and since I
want to die, I do not want it to be because of
you. I shall choose my death out of despair,
not out of anger, as I want to disappear
without hatred, that is to say without you.

Besides, death seems to me very distant:
I imagine it every night, during those long
hours when I am waiting to be overcome by
sleep, just as at one time I used to imagine
you, knowing that you would never come
to wrench me away from myself, from these
thoughts which trap me, from this body

which is a stranger to me. So I continue today to lock myself into impossible desires, despising myself for being unable either to live them out or to forget them.

And whilst I am meditating on my own mediocrity, Emmanuelle drives three hundred kilometers to get the firearms which were in father's trunk, and she calls the fire brigade before shooting herself in the throat, so that it does not fall to me to discover her body. So here I stand before her as I stand before you: totally fascinated by the greatness of her action, whilst at the same time being infinitely wounded by it.

Not only have I lost her, but with her death she adds to the ranks of the ghosts which have weighed me down since birth. When I was ten years old, I used to dream of delicate, transparent cloths, white and vaporous, hovering all around me: these were the souls of the dead which floated above my bed, and which condemned me to stay there, motionless, and filled with fear. All these departed ones, never completely absent, seemed to be your emissaries, charged with the task of binding me to

my childhood, without running the risk
of actually showing themselves. From deep
within your convent you commanded an army
of phantoms, who attacked me treacherously
in my sleep. Henceforth Emmanuelle is in
your camp, in spite of herself and in spite
of you.

I shall gradually forget her, whatever my
efforts, but suddenly, when I am being
particularly thoughtless, she comes back to
my heart, like a blow from an invisible fist,
leaving me breathless, my muscles flaccid,
my legs trembling, and a gaping black hole
behind my eyes. I repeat to myself very
loudly: 'She is dead, she is dead, she is
dead' – as if this truth could protect me
from an enemy which only exists deep within
myself.

Thus all the ones who have departed
are hostile to me, and always knock me
down, because I have been weak enough
to want their presence. And you who out-
strip all of them, you have been power-
less to protect me from my own desires
and from the indifference of others. Your
love, therefore, has served only to arm me

against myself. Will I one day be able to make use of these arms, as Emmanuelle did, in order to escape finally from your domination?

I have flung myself into a foolish battle, and your silence weighs heavily on me. How can I pursue someone who is for ever slipping away? Why do I shout whilst you remain silent? I thought I might protect myself from you by talking to you from a distance, whilst you were unable to reply to me; but the outpourings of my own heart betray me, and I have nothing which can stem them. You have prayer for your refuge, but I am always surrounded by my ghosts.

I was brought up in a good school, however. Three years of a fascist and Catholic education in Spain taught me all the prayers that I needed to rid myself of evil thoughts – one prayer for going upstairs, one prayer for coming down, one prayer whilst waiting for the bus, a sign of the cross before diving into the swimming pool. My love for you is basically just the perverted residue of a thought, stolen from God; and, like God, it has assumed increasingly disguised forms from age to age.

First, I expected from you an odour by which to orientate myself in the hostile world where my mother had abandoned me; then I sought a breast to suckle me, arms to cradle me, a voice to lull me to sleep. But I got none of those things, and my childhood never recovered from my having been of necessity torn from the body which bore me.

Later, when all you could give me was your attention, I continued, without knowing it, to seek in you a protective covering which would determine the limits of my body and of my despair. The more aware I became of the impossibility of this, the more I wanted to melt into you. I thought that perhaps other embraces would deliver me from you, but I was forgetting that absence and fear find permanent hiding places in the wounds of the past.

Finally I became more reasonable, resigning myself to being, at least in my dreams, no longer someone sick to the point of death and capable of being revived through you.

I accepted the need to force back my desire into words, into this terrible apartness of bodies which have to stand upright and alone, hanging by a rationale which pretends to ignore their existence. I really tried hard to expect nothing from you other than this spiritual communion. I no longer resented your austere habit of demonstrating that you were different from other women. I no longer resented your perpetual retreats, and your prayers for me, which held me, but never close to you. I had finally accepted that I could only meet you on the bare plains of discussion, from which I could no longer be driven by the demons of temptation. I wanted to explore new sensations, without memory and without guilt . . .

I was forgetting that some words can go right through us, and can be imbued with desire just like the flesh. So I would always expect something more from our exchanges, from this verbal intimacy that rekindled a desire which was absolute, devoid of carnality, permanently protected from the wear and tear of the body. I had fought against the physical violence which drew me towards you, and I believed that, thanks to this asceticism, I had earned happiness.

But gradually you forced me out of this paradise by obstinately avoiding confidences. At the end of this road that I had travelled in the hope of reaching you without touching you, you closed the door on me once more.

Perhaps I shall understand you eventually, but do not count on me to forgive you, whilst day after day I have to pay within my own body for the destitution in which you left me.

You always had excellent excuses for evading me, and when you could not find any, I even made them up for you. I took your side against myself, as you had succeeded in making me believe that love was unselfish – just another of your virtuous theories which propped up my infantilism, helping me to go forward but always on crutches, always limping. Instead of asking myself what made me happy, I spent my time assessing the amount of love to which I had a right; and all your desultory smiles through the grilles in the parlour, between absences, never allowed me to get my breath back. I should have fled from you, but I did not have the courage, and

I grew accustomed to being ill after each of our meetings.

Sometimes, just to catch sight of you was enough to bring tears to my eyes, but I feigned indifference simply to appear normal. And the more I was deprived of you, the more invasive my desire became. Where a few words of affection might have sufficed, after weeks or sometimes months of waiting I became insatiable. Then everything began to blur in my mind: everything, from words to skin, was mingled in one fused desire.

I would doubtless have found my place near you if you had been physically more present, at least when you were actually there. It seemed almost as though you did not have a body. Admittedly you are not as stiff and awkward as I am, but when I do embrace you I seem to have nothing in my hands: your presence vanishes behind an attractive appearance. My lips brush your cheek and feel nothing; you are a hollow body, without warmth and without substance. There is nothing mutual in our kisses. You take nothing from me, you give nothing to me, I do not exist, but I am full of pain.

You continued always to draw me to you, and then to block, one after the other, all the paths which might have allowed me to reach you. You stimulated my natural instincts, but when they led me towards you, you stayed hidden in shadow; you encouraged me to reflect on my own life, and then you reproached me for becoming introspective; you pushed me towards the people who taught and formed me, but when I started to enthuse and to ask questions about life and the world, you thought I was becoming an intellectual; and this description, so contemptuous of all the hurt which I had been trying to conceal from you, pierced me like a dagger.

What then really were you, with your prayers disguised as dialogue, your winning smiles, and your open arms which only served to keep you at a distance? You took an interest in me in the hope of shaping a creature in your own image: and the result might appear satisfactory to you, but to me it is unbearable.

Your body and your voice, therefore, often contradicted the affection which you claim to have for me. And so I had to summon up all the resources of my imagination to create a language which my heart could not grasp. In this way I entered the magic world of words, a deceptive refuge where I believed I was re-creating you for my own personal use. But all I did was to lose you and to delude myself, becoming each day more incapable of living either with you or without you.

How many times, when I have been close to you, my legs have trembled as you rocked to its foundations the fragile equilibrium I had so painstakingly created. I scarcely dared raise my eyes to look at you, for fear of disintegrating; and the silence terrified me even more.

Yet this desire for you had little to do with love, even though it burned like love. Had it been so, and had I been able to, I would happily have led you astray in spite of the distance between us, and in spite of your vow of solitude. I have no more respect for you than I have for myself, and I would have been prepared to compromise you, if I could have been sure that my boldness would have made me loved, and that this love would have fulfilled me.

Why am I not blind and all-powerful, like one of Racine's heroes, to force you to love me, or to kill you in a dazzling burst of hatred? Alas, I have no power over you. But I am clear-sighted, and I feel instinctively that this need I have for you is merely the imprint in my flesh of an incomplete childhood. It is the grief for my mother that I want to melt away in your arms. Even if I could hold you in a passionate embrace, I know that after a few months my mother's absence would interpose itself once more; and I shall never become an adult by trying to forget her. Nor is it any sense of morality which makes my love life so exemplary in its fidelity: it is only the acute perception of my infantile desires which ties me to other women.

For you are not the only one to react to my inadequacies. In the midst of your silence women take shape, women who talk to me and who look at me, women with whom I can quieten what torments me, to the point when my dragons can be put to rest and I can even tame the doves of friendship. And we laugh together, and they put their hand on my shoulder, and I can clasp them in my arms; and sometimes, after several years, I can even enjoy their presence without being prostrated by their departure. But initially I have paid for months, through nights of tears, for each one of these women; I have been consumed by sobbing, by death wishes, and even racked by vomiting in case any one of them should know how much I wanted her.

Perhaps I might have suffered less if I had dared say it to them, but I could not run the risk that they loved me as poorly as I loved them. The adult in me, therefore, already lives in the affection of someone cherished. What I miss is a mother; and you are better placed than anyone to recall that for me.

None of the women I have loved has ever been as present in my mind as you have

been since my childhood, none has been
so marvellous, or so desirable, and none
has stayed so distant either. Some have left
my life, others share from time to time the
better part of me. When I am with them,
freed finally fom my obsessions, I get the
feeling of having built something; with you
I am always in ruins.

And yet I asked nothing special of you. I
simply wanted to know that you were less
blind than I, and at least understood what
I was asking for – by being with me you
were accepting the need to help me, with
your presence, to push back the dead who
are always ready to suffocate me. But how
could you possibly have done this, when you
seem to be calling to them and cherishing them
more than me?

All around you I see corpses who look like you, because you feed them with your sorrow. If I stopped idealising you in my desire, would you become as terrifying as they are?

No, you would not; for you are beautiful. It is I who am all wrinkled inside. It is not age which is afflicting me, it is hatred which is gnawing me away. In writing to you I wanted to bring out everything that was inside me, but I can find nothing but anger – no redeeming childhood, no innocence to be reborn.

Do you remember the day I was thirteen, when you kissed me to wish me a happy birthday? I was sitting next to you having a meal, but I can no longer remember where it was. How could I possibly remember, obsessed as I was by the fear of betraying the emotion which was stifling me? I could see nothing beyond your cornet and the blue of your veil; and I was trembling so much I could scarcely swallow, although I gave no outward sign. After the meal, I used the first little annoyance as an excuse for losing my temper. My father made as if to give me a smack. He never had the courage to hit us; it was enough for him just to hate us, when he could no longer bear the absence of my mother. You always coaxed me in order to calm me down. But your tenderness was offered at a time when I was incapable of accepting it. And in any event, you did not give it freely: for you it was less a question of loving me than of making me forget my bad temper. Momentarily I was undecided: should I continue with my tantrums, and so perhaps run the risk of your scolding me? Or should I swallow down my anger in exchange for a smile? Even then I was venal and I capitulated. But that evening, alone in my bed, I wept in despair because I had not had the courage to face your disapproval.

Now, years later, I can face it. I want you to give me the bill for your affection which ostensibly was so free and unconstrained, but which in fact was hidden behind good intentions, prizes of affection, and interest carefully calculated on the basis of a virtuous future for Emmanuelle and myself. Your exactness disgusts me: you were not prepared to die for us, as Christ did on the cross, so you should have given us a choice. I had no need of imaginary props to hold me up, I simply wanted to be left lying down. Just remember this: I refused any nourishment after mother's death until you took me in your arms. At the age of ten I was so thin that you advised my father to send me to the country, and then I guzzled enough for four! When I returned you thought I was looking well, and I just wanted to throw up everything I had gorged myself with.

You were never cut out to play the part of a foster-mother, so why did you ever try? You were anxious that I should live, of course! It made life much easier for you! You did not snatch me from the jaws of death, but you held my head just above the water, so as to avoid the blame which would have weighed on you had I disappeared. Now you can weep for Emmanuelle, but I have no more tears: I envy her too much, and I despise myself for my own cowardice.

I know that I shall get some breaks in the depression I am in, but as soon as I have the strength I shall use it to destroy myself, as I always do, so that I refute every single moment of happiness. I have never been able to conclude a conversation which seemed to involve me in happiness without feeling sick or being overwhelmed with anger. In spite of myself, my body has taken its revenge for the warmth which for a few hours led me, dazzled though I was, to the brink of death. It was not life you gave back to me: it was permanent remorse, in the midst of which I built for myself a ridiculous and implacable morality which looked like you.

You should not have thrown me back into life; you should not have just half-loved me. You should have withdrawn into your convent and let me sink down, like Emmanuelle, into darkness and silence.

The basic cowardice is accepting life: no compromise is worse than that one. From that point onwards, all morality has to be reinvented.

I envy Emmanuelle, I envy her courage in taking her madness to its logical conclusion. The shot she fired is the only appropriate response to the triumphant smile of those self-satisfied women who litter the world with their terrified offspring. It is true that you yourself have refrained from giving life to urchins who had not asked for anything. For you it was enough to pick up the pieces. And what style you did it with! You almost succeeded single-handed in repeating the miracle of the Holy Trinity: a father and a son joining together platonically to give birth to a Holy Spirit. No woman, no sex: pure, solid divinity! You are not God, and yet without copulation, and without shedding so much as a single drop of blood, you gave life to the bad spirit that I have become.

Yesterday evening I saw a photograph of you: you were holding me in your arms, and you looked exultant. You were already wearing your habit, to make it clear to the rest of mankind that you were not quite part of their world, but you were clasping me to your heart as if to prove that you could do the same as other women. What joy for you to be able to play at virgin-mother! Martyrdom for my sake – thank you so much! A fairly gentle martyrdom, of course; just enough to keep up appearances. For quite a number of years, because of you, I thanked God for the gift of life. Now that God has disappeared from my perspective, swept away first by my anger and then by my indifference, it is you that I have to thank for it.

Thank you for having decided from the lofty heights of your own certainties to snatch me from the death into which I was gently slipping so as to find rest; thanks to you I have lost it forever.

Thank you for having once held me in your arms to feed me; through you I recovered my appetite, and ever since whatever I swallow makes me ill.

Thank you for having taught me through your example to respect and love my neighbour, with whom I have a good relationship for a few hours each week; for the rest of the time I despise and loathe myself.

Thank you for having encouraged my intellectual aspirations: I almost succeeded in making other people believe I was intelligent; and now I know that will not help me either.

Thank you finally for loving me as you have. I hope that today you have a strong sense of everything I owe you. However, the ill that I wish you can hurt you only in the future, whereas your love has destroyed me, very slowly, from the very first day.

Does your hell still exist? Does your religion reject the everlasting flames promised for those who are damned? Or does it enjoy lighting gehennas to terrify those whose only wish is to disappear? Personally, I no longer have any fear of hell, I have plunged into it. From there I wish you ill, boundless, immeasurable ill, knowing full well that I can never reach you. My hatred will disturb you as little as my love, and I know you will never let yourself be damaged by my feelings. I can certainly cause you suffering, but I could never make you as base as I am, nor force you to loathe me or to scorn me. You will continue to regard me as a human being, whereas all I want to be is a source of ill. Alas, you will always escape me, because even if by chance I was in the process of actually killing you, you would already have forgiven me.

If I could be like you, my pain would be

less. I am, by the way, sometimes like you
when I am with others. In fraternal moments
such as these I get intense enjoyment from the
generosity and goodwill which spring from
a feeling of deep reconciliation between the
world and myself. This is the underground
spring from which intelligence flows – this
trusting lucidity which passes like a flash of
lightning or like an open hand through all the
hard outer shells of life . . .

But each one of these moments ends for me
with a revival of my pain. As I have already
said to you: the richer the mutuality of a
relationship, the more the separation hurts
me. Far away from an understanding glance,
from a voice which calms me by mingling
together the threads in the deep-rooted net-
work of a forgotten childhood, I sense anger
rising inside me until it crushes my brain and
stifles my heart. I feel so ill that I am angry
with myself for having allowed myself some
happiness, forgetting that I would pay for it
so dearly. The suffering puts me back on the
see-saw of childhood distress and I feel once
more, in the very depths of my flesh, the cries
and the rage in which I hid myself, hoping in

vain that you would come and take me in
your arms.

You had already gone back to God, and
I learned, in self-defence, that life can only
be won with blows of fury and despair. I
try now in vain to convince myself that
burning and shouting are of no avail: but
my body has forgotten nothing, and reverts
after each separation to the horrible reflex of
my childhood, to the time when you gave me
back my life like a poisoned chalice.

I would like to go far away, to unfasten the iron collar of my childhood which always brings me back to you, my heart tied and bound. I would like to rediscover what my life was like without you, when I was growing up in Spain, where I experienced new sensations through voices which were quite different from yours. I would like to fall back once again into that marvellous interlude, in which I believed I could be reborn without memory.

At the age of sixteen I discovered a foreign language which soothed me. When people talked to me, all I had to do was to unravel what they were saying, instead of trying agonisingly to discover in your words the things you had not wanted to say to me.

For several years now I have been learning Corneille and Racine by heart. I gulped them down in large draughts, until I was almost drunk, and they helped me to forget your empty sentences, which I could not assimilate. I understood very little of the speeches, but they fascinated me as they pulled me towards something terrifying buried deep within me. But in Spain the lure of the abyss was transformed into exuberance in the midst of the free, unconstrained words which burst forth all around me.

I made a friend called Nieves. Her name, meaning 'snow', burned my lips when I said it quietly to myself, in the darkness of a corridor. I added to it little disconnected phrases, sips of affectionate diminutives which I had gleaned from here and there. These words, whose meaning I was uncertain of, took me back to the dawn of language, to that paradise before reason began, when maternal voices are woven all around us, like a cocoon of saliva and silk.

Nieves was Catalan. Exiled from her own regional language by Franco, she had been sent to a French grammar-school by her grandparents who demonstrated in this way their resistance to the tyranny of Spain. I learned later that her mother had married one of Franco's officers, in spite of family disapproval. Since the death of her parents in an accident, Nieves lived with her grandparents who spoke to her in French; she replied in Spanish, and in this way she too tried to hold her own with her past.

We scarcely ever left each other, even during the holidays which we spent together in Castille. I loved this part of the country where groups of people lived together, almost as if in a seraglio. Occasionally, by a stretch of water, in the shade of a thicket, a woman taking her ease beneath her white parasol would receive her son's friends, greeting each one with a few nonchalant and gracious words, using an infinite number of variations. In a nearby clearing forty places had been set for the young people, using silver plates and cutlery, and servants dressed in white jackets would later bring in enormous platters of *tostones*, sucking pigs roasted to perfection. This ostentatious show from a bygone age gave an impression of decadence, of a disintegrating world; and I could see also, inside the shaded house, servant girls younger than I who were on their knees scrubbing the floor.

You were far away, very far away from this life, which had nothing in common with what you had taught me. I was finally forgetting you, and learning to breathe.

Nieves continued to take me far away from you. One day she told me she no longer believed in God. I was shattered, particularly as in the early days her religious fervour had helped to bring us together.

We often visited churches, even during the week, and the liturgies enchanted me – I knew no pleasure more exquisite than murmuring the daily prayers on our knees, in an almost empty chapel, under the agonized gaze of an enormous, emaciated Christ on the cross. The faith that you had passed on to me and in which, when alone, I had lost my way, through pride, through folly, now began to make sense to me, and brought me closer to Nieves. When I was with her, I no longer tried to conquer myself, to disarm myself. I was no longer paralysed by the fear of causing her to leave me. I almost dared to breathe without thinking that I was a dragon, and that my breath might destroy her.

On the 8th of December one year, after a candlelight procession in honour of the Immaculate Conception, we both stayed to pray in the darkened church, joined together beneath the circle of light from our flickering candles. Nieves started to sing my favourite canticle for me: '*Salve Regina, mater misericordiae.*'

In this moment of pure ecstasy my religious fervour was lost in my love for her, and I would gladly have become a martyr to give a divine halo to my carnal rapture. I no longer doubted either God or the world, and I blessed the religion which had transformed a loving friendship into an act of faith. For without the help of these prayers I would never have dared to abandon myself to the bursting joy of my heart.

What would happen to me if she were to leave me alone in these churches? What would I do with all this fervour which could no longer be shared?

Was it faith that I lost with Nieves, or was it just the fascination of a mystical and obscure language? As my prayers ebbed away, so too did my innocence, and my murmurs of love were no longer expressed in long psalms which had given a broader, deeper life to my feelings. These prayers, which went through me and then beyond me, became the banal confessions of an adolescent in the throes of seduction, and I wasted away in my guilt. My words no longer had flesh, my thoughts about Nieves were devoid of imagination, and, as with you, I plunged into solitude and shame.

Even today I can no longer hear the whispered sounds of the world around me. I can no longer sense behind my distress a universal lamentation capable of transforming this monotonous dirge into a vast polyphony.

Nieves had put away her missal, and had
plunged into the study of history. She opened
her books on the table between us, and
we read, in French, stories of the civil
war. At the age of seventeen how could
we resist the collapse of a world that our
imagination had built up around a faultless
mother and father? We discovered first of
all the dead of the battlefields, for whom
Franco had erected a huge concrete cross in
the 'Valle de los Caidos': this overlooked
an arid landscape, and it stood alone, as
if it were a Don Quixote shining out over
the plain of La Mancha ravaged by a brown
plague.

Death stretched out as far as the eye could
see, in this Spain which was so stained with
blood, just like the memories of my birth.
Even the smell of blood seemed familiar to
us: it was already rancid, and overhung the

musty odours of chlorine and burning ruins.
But next to these corpses there were others,
silently buried in communal graves at the
foot of gibbets. As we turned the pages we
saw thousands of men in chains, taken from
prisons at dawn to be shot against a wall, or
garrotted.

And the church to which you belong
greeted the new order by singing Te Deums.
A bishop to the army even cried: 'Blessed
be the cannon which open breeches to let
the gospel through!' What happened to these
crusaders who were going to rescue the country from the barbarians? We could recognise
nothing in these histories of Spain. No high
feats of arms, no carnivorous, illiterate or
heathen armies, no rebel generals hiding a
father's pain in a heroic heart: 'Sin novedad en
el Alcazar!' Seen through the eyes of a defeated
people, the war looked really sinister. It was
impossible for Nieves to take any pride in her
father's part in it. Could there be any heroes
at all after a nation had been crushed? Forty
peasants shot in Andalusia because one bull
was killed!

Is no one left in Andalusia?
In the mountains of Andalusia,
Is anyone still there?
In the seas and fields of Andalusia
Is anyone still there?

The voice of the poet had no echo other than
the dead . . .

How could you ever have understood the exaltation which enabled me finally to reconcile my ideals and my subconscious needs? I was cursing a tyrant who had reduced Spain to silence, I had nothing but scorn for a religion which had brought a people to its knees, and I had a friend who, like me, had learned painfully how to deny what she had previously loved. For the first time my hatred did not plunge me back into solitude, but put me instead in harmony with a world where you did not exist.

It was then that I discovered the joys of secrecy, of those half hidden exchanges, of those unspoken agreements to share rebellious and generous ideas with someone of the same heart and mind, and they seemed to us quite separate from our physical attachment. These furtive mutual understandings, which circulated under cover of the leaden mantle of formal lectures, generated immeasurable vibrations within us, in the face of people, like yourself, who never felt anything.

A few of our teachers, with protective enthusiasm, sustained this unspoken but shared knowledge and rebelliousness. And so there evolved between adults and adolescents a hidden web of solidarity which shone through all the classes. We were hungry for knowledge, as everything we learned united us against the paternal figure of Caudillo, hated and ever-present.

Half way through the year one of our teachers disappeared from school, and I had the impression, in spite of the fact that you were so far away, that it was your blind hypocrisy that had been responsible for this injustice. You were in the enemy camp, not because of what you had said or done, but because you simply ignored what was happening around you.

Later it got worse: I began to understand that, even in France, you had never seen anything. The generous intentions of your prayers were the best possible excuse for your blindness. Instead of praying for others, you would have done better to look at them.

I remember a workshop of grease, metal and concrete, in which thirty grey, speechless women worked who were stupefied, as I was, with fatigue and deafened by the noise of the motors. An enormous press pounded my exhaustion five thousand times a day, forcing me into a continuous repetition of automatic movements. And whilst I pressed metal bars, endlessly, beneath an iron column which banged down indifferently, the girl next to me was weeping softly into her machine, without slowing down the rhythm of her work.

What can you hear from behind your convent walls, you who claim to listen to the world? You have spent years saying useless words to me, whilst the world which you believed you were sustaining with your prayers was sinking into silence.

You have unquestionably learned nothing about other people or about me. But I no longer hold this against you, and in future will speak to you from far away.

Nieves and I had entered into the world of adults with our hearts weighed down, since our parents, amongst whom I included you, had abandoned us and for our inheritance had left us an obsolete ideal in which we could no longer believe.

We therefore sought other support amongst the downtrodden, amongst those who hated you with a fervour which was equalled only by your prayers. Far removed from your good intentions, they showed us a path paved with torments. So, for example, Dolores Ibarruri, la Pasionara, kept us awake for three nights, as we read her memoirs by the light of a lamp under the bedsheets. She was as vibrant as only a woman can be, but she fought like a man; Nieves nestled against me, in this moving and luminous grotto of bedclothes, and with her arms she completed the circle in which I was being reborn, upheld by

the mysterious murmuring of a decimated
people, who were slowly rebelling, in silence
and in exile.

You undoubtedly belong to the race of
permanent victors, those pleasant and cour-
teous executioners of peacetime, who kill
by omission. You never knew what you had
killed in me, which in spite of Nieves is now
lost for ever. I found love again, but not peace
of mind. Pleasure is a currency in which the
devil deals, and it has cost me dear: embraces
end torn apart, and death always manages to
slip away.

It is only anger which never lets me
down. The anger I shared with Nieves was
boundless. One day, our cry: 'Franco the
assassin!' burst through the topmost peaks
of the Sierra, and rang out to the stars,
carried by an avenging echo. The moun-
tain itself seemed to be rebelling against an
empty sky. We gazed at each other, and
marvelled. Never had our hatred found such
a powerful expression in a setting of such
grandeur.

I believed then that I was healed – of you, of
your insipid whispering, of my own narrow

frustrations . . . I did not know that even my Spanish adventure would fall back into your net.

For three years Nieves and I had not been separated. We had progressed from genuflections to raised fists, from fervour to fury, from solitude to solidarity. The future looked straightforward, and the decisions I had taken irrevocable. But my father returned to work in France, and after the exams came the summer of separations.

I savoured every day, to the point of obsession, forcing myself not to think of what would follow; and at night I fought the onset of sleep, because behind my closed eyelids there opened a vast black hole.

Shortly before the start of the academic year which was going to part us finally, we came back to see you with Emmanuelle and my father. I entered the convent like a conquering hero, giving the parlour a distant glance, as though I had outgrown it. The gleaming woodwork of the windows, which opened out onto flower-beds, smelt of pickled devotion and warm polish. I preferred the smell of olive oil and fried onions in the little Spanish alleys, where life teemed and screeched from every direction. How many families heaped together in one room could you have housed properly within your walls? Your God occupied all your dwelling place, and this pure spirit, though taking up so much of it, still remained invisible.

Hanging from his gallows, he seemed to spread his calvary across your walls, and I recognised then in that bleeding face, in that mouth twisted with pain, in that wounded side, all the crucified piety of my childhood. My anger also found echoes in this agony. Nieves and I were both still absorbed by it, knowing full well that the real victims never recovered. But our enjoyment of Spanish poetry extended beyond the narrow boundaries of our convictions. Standing in front of this crucifix, mystical poems came back to our mind. At one time we used to recite them like secret declarations of love, when our effusions could no longer be contained by analysis and reason. We started together to say:

'No me mueve, mi Dios, para quererte
el cielo que me tienes prometido,
ni me mueve el infierno tan temido . . .'

and when we then hesitated, you came up
to us, put your hand on my shoulder, and
continued:

'para dejar por eso de ofenderte.'

With this one line you caught me in your
net once more, and at one stroke you took
away from me my three best years: you
broke the secret language which joined me
to Nieves, and you hung the dead weight of
my childhood around my neck. Even before
I glared at you in fury, you could feel my
anger in the stiffness of my shoulder, and
you moved away, murmuring: 'Excuse me,
I did not mean to interrupt you.'

But it was too late. The holidays came to
an end; Nieves went back to her own country;
I decided not to take up the study of Spanish;
and since that time I have scarcely ever spoken
the language.

Monday 25 March

One whole day without writing to you, without renewing my hatred for you, and once
again I am completely defenceless. I make
excuses for you, I take your side, I mellow
into goodwill, and I feel myself getting old.

You could hardly be held responsible for the
despair into which I was plunged after Nieves
had left. How could I have understood then
that this separation was going to force me
back to the agonies of a terrified childhood?
Once again my flesh could scarcely contain
my feelings, and I felt as though I had been
dismembered. I hardened myself as best I
could, forgetting everything that Nieves had
taught me. With her I had discovered that the
body is just a machine for crushing painful
emotions. When she was near me, I felt
alive; when she kissed me, when she held
my hand, my skin no longer crawled with
fear. I felt solid, I no longer felt that I was

being emptied like a burst leather bottle; and when she spoke to me, her voice flowed into me like sap bringing me back to my roots.

I was far away from you, far away from your affectionate words spoken to keep me at a distance. But you are only a pretext for my anger. I know now that at each separation I shall have to face not only the absence of the other person, but also the splitting of myself into two. And my aggression is one way of unburdening myself from this other me, whom I detest. But maybe you are unaware of the existence of this other person, you who claim to love me completely?

Yesterday I re-read the sonnet attributed to St John of the Cross, and I spent hours translating it before I realised that this transition from Spanish to French was a bridge that I was building between Nieves and you, between the two parts of me which for so long have been irreconcilable.

I am copying it out for you today, clearly without the same faith that you have – but behind this literary work you will sense, I hope, a fervour which you have never been able to understand.

Anonimo
(Siglo XVI)
(Atribuido a San Juan de la Cruz)

Soneto

No me mueve, mi Dios, para quererte
el cielo que me tienes prometido,
ni me mueve el infierno tan temido
para dejar por eso de ofenderte.

Tú me mueves, Señor, muéveme el verte
clavado en una cruz y escarnecido,
muéveme ver tu cuerpo tan herido,
muévenme tus afrentas y tu muerte.

Muévenme, en fin, tu amor, y en tal manera,
que aunque no hubiera cielo, yo te amara,
y aunque no hubiera infierno, te temiera.

No me tienes que dar porque te quiera,
pues aunque lo que espero no esperara,
lo mismo que te quiero te quisiera.

What makes me, Lord, love you always
   so dear
Is not that future life, which I implore;

Nor is it hell – which yet fills me with
    fear –
That forces me not to offend you more.

'Tis you, my God, who force me to that
    place
Where, nailed upon a cross, sore pain your
    part,
I see again your anguish, and your face
Whose image deep within me moves my
    heart.

Your love alone makes me near you to
    dwell,
I'd love you, and for after-life care nought:
The fear of you I know, though not belief
    in hell.

All I need to love you is your love,
And if reward were hoped for, though not
    sought,
I'd love you more than ever I could prove.

Our separation haunted me for months. I found Nieves' absence unbearable, and at the same time I started to grow desperate that I would end by getting used to it. I watched myself smiling at new friends, with whom I would forget her, and even before this happened I was reproaching myself for my fickleness and cowardice. I did not feel that by neglecting her I was harming her: it was myself I was hurting by accepting my own denial, by allowing to die what had been the better part of me for three years.

During the following vacation I did not see her. I was too unstable. Had I seen her again I would surely have spent whole nights in tears, and would then have been even more disgusted with myself. How many times must I betray my friends and betray myself in order to plunge wholeheartedly into a routine daily life? I would have liked to lock myself away

in an ivory tower, so as not to be distracted
by new and sympathetic acquaintances, who
wrenched me away from my memories.

I am reminded of an old, affectionate servant, always ready to put her arms around me.
Well turned out, pink-cheeked and comfortable, she was everything I could have wanted,
and I really liked her. And yet I did not
yield to her persuasiveness. The nearer she
came to me, the further I moved away. She
laughed, but never insisted. One day you
saw me. Perhaps at that time you respected
my rejection of this feeling, of which I was
unaware. Perhaps I only loved you because
you kept your distance. I was so near to
death during the first hours of my life, that
for a long time I was nervous of anyone who
came near me.

Only Nieves, speaking to me in an unknown
language, had been able to find a significant
chink in the armour I had made for myself.
She gathered me silently from somewhere that
pre-dated memory, to which you had not yet
bound me after the death of my mother. For
her, I did not have to prove myself worthy of
anything. There was no promise of eternity

to weigh me down. She was not interested in my soul, or in my future. She was not interested in trying to be good for me, but she did me an enormous amount of good. Her love was direct, egotistical, unpremeditated: and it freed me from myself, from the self that was always tense in anticipation of trying to please you. With her I could be impulsive, demanding, relaxed; she loved me for my rebelliousness, and my laziness, she loved me because I loved her, and I asked for nothing in return. Thanks to her I could be reborn, from the earliest days of my childhood. Of all the women I have wanted, she is the only one whom I have never tried to seduce with words.

After I returned to France, my native tongue became the crucible of my joys, the very flesh of my desire. I built a hiding-place for myself at the heart of the language: voices caressed me, and words touched me. But behind the rustle of life, I could always hear the rattle of death.

Yet your voice drew me away, to more peaceful places, when you took me on your knee to comfort me. Why did you want me

to grow up, if not to be independent of you?
And, later, could you not sense that behind
my fear of approaching you was the need to
be cherished?

Writing to you brings me very slowly out of a nightmare, but I am afraid of being suddenly engulfed in it again without warning. Besides, I know I am playing with fire, and in the course of my probing I am finding, once again, agonies whose roots go very deep.

My childhood bursts in upon my nights, into that twilight area where dreams consist of forgotten memories. And so I live out once more the first few hours of my life in the hospital where I was born . . .

. . . All is confusion. I am lost in smells and sounds, and have nothing to hold on to. But the click of heels strikes regularly on the tiles, like the footsteps of death, now coming nearer, now moving further away. I try again to find my mother's body, with its smell of torn flesh, but all I am conscious of is the musty smell of leather and benzine, which takes me far away from her, into a world where I am utterly lost. I shout out, I cry, and then I feel myself being held by arms which cradle me and which smell good.

My father leaves the room. The steel tips on his heels no longer hurt my ears, and I am no longer imprisoned in his leather-jacketed grasp. Someone puts me down next to my mother: I am in familiar country, my senses close gently, and I fall asleep.

When I awake I am enveloped in dampness, warm and sweet. Life is flowing near me, filling me softly with delirium: my mother is bathed in her own blood. And suddenly everything snaps. I am torn away from her warmth; the metallic steps start again in my head; and the stifling, sour smell of leather covers me like a leaden mantle. I cannot breathe, I am afraid, I scream, and a shroud closes over me. So I stay silent, not moving, mouth shut, fists tight clenched; I stay there prostrate, tense, cut off from the world, motionless, so as to be safe.

Never again will I feel life flowing next to me. Never again will I dare let myself go, and let my own body, too, be emptied. I must now hold back everything, to protect myself. Nothing moves inside me, neither nourishment nor feelings, which are buried deep in my belly and my head. I dare not fall asleep again, for fear that I am emptied, and my life slips away.

Never again will I know the smell of my mother. My father has killed her; and if I let him near me, if I move or I cry, perhaps he will come back and bury me alive in a black leather vault. But when the sound of his heels has stopped hurting my head and filling me with terror, maybe it will be my turn to disappear gently, as my mother did, bathed in death.

But then one day you came along and mixed up the scent.

Are you sure that when you took me in your arms, three days after my mother's death, you were thinking only of comforting me, of helping me get back my appetite? You certainly did not blame me for her death, but perhaps you hoped to find in me someone who might replace her? Maybe the fact that in your presence I have never felt myself, was because you were in fact looking for another person?

As I no longer knew who I was, I did not know who to love. All in all, my instincts and emotions always drew me to you, but such a love was not even thinkable. When I was close to you I used to tremble, and I thought it was because I was sick – indeed, I became sick, increasingly sick, trying to find a name for these overwhelming feelings which only you could have soothed with your caresses.

Now I am forever falling in love, but I feel

at the same time that I am stooping very low. And the more ashamed I am of these desires, the more I expect everything from them. In this way I heap disappointments one on top of the other, as if to prove that I am not worthy of being loved, and that you were right to have loved me so indifferently.

And yet God knows that I watched for the smallest sign of affection, the very least trace of your presence. Your odour, for example, confused my senses from the very earliest days: it was so like that of my mother that for a long time I doubted whether she had really disappeared. But then I could not understand why my cries did not bring her back to me. You came to see me, but never when I really needed you. Because of this, happiness and unhappiness seemed to come to me by chance, and always at the moment when I least expected them. What I was guilty of was hoping for your presence, as this hope never resulted in anything. I therefore spent my life wanting what I could never have, in order to be faithful to the unsatisfied wish of my childhood, the only one which seemed worthy of you.

I have now learned to walk on a deserted slope, where dogs howl at death next to a corpse, and as I write I feel like an animal caught in a trap.

The more I need you, the more often I think of my father. I never thought that some living feeling could exist between himself and me. And yet the fact that I waited – although always in vain – for you to love me as mother and father was surely because he too had a part to play in my life. For so long I simply did not think that. As I look back on my childhood, however, it seems to me that I was always seeking him out, at least until the day when he thrust me aside even more harshly than usual, with one of those murderous phrases for which parents seem to have a gift, and which wound the heart for ever.

I can still hear the reproach which he expressed in the cutting tones of a man secure in his own knowledge and perfection: 'When will you stop thinking you are the centre of the world?' At that moment I stopped, paralysed, whilst the whole world around me collapsed, leaving me alone in the midst of a desert.

Perhaps I might have developed differently had he loved me, but he loved his own pain too much to share it with the living. Even if I did not stop thinking of myself as the centre of the inhabited world, at least I have spared my loved ones the pretence of believing it. That did not make me happy, but it enabled me to think I was. And it is true that you did want so very much the happiness of other people that it is hard for you to imagine they have not attained it.

Three men came into my dreams last night. I
wanted to cry for help, but no sound would
come. I awoke in a sweat. This was not the
first time that they had intruded into my sleep,
and I would like to have wrung their necks,
theirs and some other people's, before they
made me retch.

A dog was eyeing me, its head terrifying,
and I was sitting in a baby chair, almost
at floor level. Three men in uniform were
talking to my father, in a harsh, unfamiliar
language. The jet-black dog was watching
me with its moist eyes, its head on a level
with mine . . . And suddenly men's voices
assailed my ears, just as they did when I
was born, the click of heels echoed on the
tiles, and once again I could smell leather.
My mother had disappeared, and in her
place was a large, hairy dog. Was it this
that was going to replace her? Was it this

horrible beast that was going to be with me day after day?

Poor Blackie. So it was he who was the source of so many of my nightmares, the dog who had been my childhood friend. He used to knock me to the ground with one stroke of his tail, and then I would hold on to him to pull myself up.

This, then, was one of those memories which evoked both pleasure and fear. Why must these two emotions be so mixed up together? Why do they always fill my heart with confusion? Your odour sometimes mingled with that of my father, above my cradle; and beneath your twofold presence, I found desire and anguish mingled together.

For years I have exhausted myself trying to split up what life had mixed together. Even today I would prefer not to both love you and hate you at the same time, but how can I fill in the gap which you have dug between us, without putting into it what is destroying me?

Monday 1 April

Telling you what I have never revealed to you, what you always preferred to ignore, is not enough to calm me; guilt still holds me firm in its embrace. It was always reflected in the eyes of my father who, on the occasions he looked at me, was seeking another face; it was even on your own lips when you kissed me by proxy. I had no need of your excuses, nor for you to understand my crises of anger and my anxieties. I would have preferred you to strike me rather than use me merely as a means of regretting the absence of your sister.

I spend my life hoping for death because I know that, much as I hope to be loved, I cannot plunge night and day into the very depths of your heart, and into the depths of my father's thoughts, unless I disappear for ever, like my mother.

And yet this desire for death, this call to

death, did not stand in isolation. At the same time you were driving me towards life, with all the force of your prayers, and in order to please you I was forced to live twice. Your expectation was so great that I could never match it. How could I be your sister, your twin, your mirror, when all I wanted to be was your child? If you had loved me less, my life would not have been so hard to bear. We often possess weapons which we can use to resist the malice of others, but we can scarcely ever restrain their love.

That does not erase my guilt. But behind this pain-filled adult, wanting to offer herself to a symbolic mother, I feel a sort of compassion for the child I once was, and I am learning now day by day how to become my own mother. This slow birthing process banishes my childish terrors, but I cannot prevent myself from expecting just a little more from you than your affection.

In the meantime I am moving away from Emmanuelle, and from her memory. Must I betray her, too, like all the women I have

loved, and with whom I have had to break
off? In ceasing to be fascinated by her suicide,
I feel that I am disowning her . . .

Nieves has written to me. We have maintained our contact in spite of the fact that we are separated from each other, and with the passing of time the passionate love which I felt for her has become a steadier friendship, although still full of wonder. My body began gradually to accept this separation, perhaps because, with her, I never felt the necessity to hate myself.

However, this detachment was still full of pain. When on previous occasions I used to cross the frontier, I would feel the fever of an adolescent forced into inactivity. I was bound to her, even in the language I used: it was not Spanish which I had learned, but her particular way of speaking, with her expressions and the sound of her voice. In a word, I had reconstructed the mysterious words of childish prayers, and each word which I spoke in her language was still a secret declaration of love. I had changed my God and my petitions, but my offering remained the same: total and despairing.

Nieves had also become the archetype of my affections: often I broke off other relationships because the desire which was at the heart of them was so much less demanding than that which drove me to her.

So how is it that, as opposed to what I feel for you, I never detested her? And yet I often felt abandoned by her – when she started to speak in Catalan it seemed like a betrayal. Later on, she told me of her new love affairs: I received these confidences gladly, but I had nothing to say to her, for I loved no one as much as I loved her, and I could no longer tell her so.

If I often wept on the train which took me back to France, I never held it against her. I could not reproach her for having revealed to me feelings which I dared not imagine with you. I was lulled by her warmth, my very dreams became more tender; I no longer hated my own body because it did not cause her to turn away from me.

And yet the first time she settled down

close to me I almost jumped backwards: I was incapable of understanding that this was just a commonplace intimacy, so foreign was it to the strictness of my upbringing. And gradually pleasure brought us together. But I still believed that this physical proximity was something unique to Spain, to this country which spoke to my heart before it ever reached my mind. Subsequently it took me many years to discover that this way of being could be just as equally French, without dishonour.

I learned Spanish in three months, far away from you, but it took me over thirty years to come to the realisation that my body too had its own means of expression, which I needed to decipher. I wanted to believe that you were the cause of this, but that was no help to me: having clothed myself in fear, I now continued rigidly in my hatred. Locked up tight within my own will-power, I believed I was treading the path of virtue; what I need today is to reach the way of abandonment.

Nieves therefore gave me back my body before I was aware that it was happening or that I was being changed. And yet the memory of that happiness allowed me subsequently to rediscover physical harmony with others. Without her, I should perhaps have been broken by my own inability to bend, which far from holding me back when I fell in love simply prevented me from picking myself up again.

When I was forced to recognise my thirst for love, to be loved, my attitude became even more rigid: I had to resist to the utmost this threatening and inadmissible discovery. I was therefore more than ready to be critical: rather than face my own anguish I preferred to defy the whole world. All in all, I became an anti-fascist because I did not dare to be in love with you, or with Nieves, and because I knew in the depths of my being that adoration had to be reserved for someone dead. Loving you was for me simply condemning you to disappear, leaving me alone as always.

So I spent years holding back these desires which pulled me towards you, certain that this torrent would sweep away everything in its path. Today I untangle the skein of useless violence, and I rediscover there the certainties of my youth, for even if they were born of a total confusion of feelings they are still the better part of me. I have learned to let myself be carried along by the current, and whilst floating there to lift up my eyes to others: I can see my father and Emmanuelle who are now on the other bank, I can see Nieves whose affection warms my heart, and I can see you. For the first time I dare look at you.

You immerse yourself in the long services of Holy Week, and I think back on those interminable prayers of my childhood, which tore us from our play, from our holidays, in the middle of the afternoon, at the seaside. The washing of the feet, the Last Supper, all of that for me is just part of folklore. I respect your beliefs and your rituals, but I do not hold to them, any more than I asked you to hold to my own rebellions. If I have talked about them it is simply to show you that my path is still filled with you, and always brings me back there.

You will go to Communion, relive the first consecration: 'This is my body, this is my blood.' You will devour your God without difficulty . . . And to think that for years I tried to copy you, to approach God through you, simply because I did not dare imagine other ways of doing it; I believed that I was

mad, because I wanted to be crushed in your
embrace and consumed by your kisses. Even
so I should not have expected you to eat me
alive every day!

I am not making fun of your sacraments:
even if hatred is familiar to me, my contempt
is not directed at you, neither at you nor at
others. It is simply that I look at things in
a new way, and I would love to discover if
your divine cannibalism could shed new light
on the eternal problem of my nutrition. How
can I learn to have no more fear of what I take
in? How can I accept that my relationship with
the world need not be restricted solely to a
look or a word? How can I nourish myself in
peace, keeping the food inside me, allowing
it to work in my body, without becoming an
ogre or a demon? I did not want to swallow
anything, to take anything; I only wanted to
be held, and to be kept safe.

And I detested you as much as this body
which you could never love and which was
now taking its revenge. 'I know all about
you: how you are neither hot nor cold. I
wish you were one or the other, but since
you are neither, but only lukewarm, I will

spit you out of my mouth.' So your God spits out those who are lukewarm. I also spat you out, almost every day! For if you were consuming yourself with love in your convent, your embraces remained lukewarm for me.

Believing that I detested you, it was however myself whom I was hating; I wanted to flee from you, but I could never escape from myself. (In any event you never ceased to throw back at me the violence of a desire which you were incapable of understanding.) Instead of absorbing my reflection so that I could lose myself in you, you simply mirrored it back to me. Maybe you were right, at least I have sometimes thought so; but today I would love you to be no longer just a clean, smooth surface, impavid and impenetrable.

Good Friday used to be one of the worst days of the Easter holidays. The services lasted interminably. There was one amusing note: the little purple covers hanging over the statues made the church seem disguised. But this carnival remained icy. It had nothing to do with the silly laughter at midnight on the following day when we used to let the hot wax from our candles trickle onto the people sitting next to us.

I have known other Good Fridays, in Spain, with black processions of penitents spilling over at the foot of the walls of a fortified city. This was not theatre, or folklore, but a funereal and sinister march with voices echoing from the depths of hell, the Inquisition on the march with its train of horrors. And in the deserted streets, Civil Guards knocked at the doors of the inns to ensure that those few customers remaining were not gambling, not drinking, not singing. The guitars remained hanging on the walls, and when the tramp of the platoon was heard everyone thought of the prisons after the war when dawn fell like the blade of a guillotine.

How could I learn to sleep with this picture before my eyes, with your voice in my ear cutting to pieces any sense there was in your mundane words, where I was incapable of trying to find anything other than your love? When finally will you help rock me to sleep, without the fear of being swallowed up by the nightmares of my childhood? It is not eternal resurrection that I have need of; I want only to surrender myself to the cycle of days and of seasons, and to feel, in your nearness, the warmth return again after the cold, as dawn is born again out of darkness.

I shall not rise up from the tomb. Even if these forty letters have helped me to come a little way out of my shell, I am still trapped in my fears. It is not a new life which is starting for me, it is my life slowly tearing itself away from yours, unfolding itself little by little in a terrifying world.

Winter is over, and the homeless no longer shiver in the streets, but the small battalions of beggars are only a reflection of the starving hordes, and the fascist prisons of my youth now exist in half the countries of the world. So this is where I have been led by this long voyage of desire: to find refuge in a world which is as monstrous as that into which I was born. My rebellions have opened my heart; they have traced paths of fire in the desert of outdated morality, but they have not always taught me how to breathe when I am far away from you.

Today I can no longer bear this rootless existence, these throbbing desires overlaid by propriety. I risk perdition when I am not near you, absence from you scorches me. So please do not reject me by trying to make me believe that happiness is far beyond what I can attain.

Your heart is not bigger than my hands, your love is not stronger than my embraces, and your convictions no longer dominate my instincts; each time I think of you I would like to die, and I think about it constantly. So do not try to guess, unbeknown to me, what I am seeking. I no longer want to be like you, I no longer want to be alive, I no longer want to believe in anything, I no longer want to be beautiful or intelligent; I simply want my suffering to cease.

So, just for once, do not hide, do not invent excuses or try to find roundabout ways. Do not be content just to think of me, and to include me in your prayers along with the rest of mankind. I have not found peace, even if my anger has gone, and I still have need of you. Do not speak to me of the world, of suffering, or of beauty; speak to me of yourself, of you to me, of what you feel: fear or indifference, desire or despair. Do not write any more long sentences, too vast and too vague, which go right through me but do not hold me; your letters, vibrant with feelings of light and shade, with cheap poetry, should no longer deflect me towards an invisible goal. Come to me, take me in your words, touch me with your looks, unclench my fists in the caress of your hands, place your breath on me, and enfold me in your arms, until my whole body is at peace and, near you, opens in the warmth of your flesh.

I love you.

Madam,
Your letters have arrived here each day,
and I sense that for you they must have
been an expression of something very deep,
something essential. I regret therefore to have
to return them to you unopened, without your
aunt, to whom they were addressed, having
been able to read them. She died last Friday,
quite suddenly, having given us no indication
of the extent of her illness.

The recent death of your sister affected her
deeply, but she had no wish to seclude herself
in this bereavement, nor in that of your father,
and her thoughts were often with you, who
represented for her a life force. Your fiery
temper, sometimes furious, she would say,
both intimidated her and also, I believe,
prevented her from showing you all her
tenderness. But your sense of rebellion often
revealed new needs to her, helped her to make

continued progress and not be complacent in her certainty.

I believe that by confiding this in me she nourished the hope that I might pass it on to you, and that I would convey to you her deep affection, to which I join my prayers, knowing, alas, that this will not erase either for you, or for her Sisters, or indeed for myself, the pain of her passing away.

Sister Agnes

Paris, April 1984 – April 1987